Top Tunes for Violin

Kevin Mayhew

We hope you enjoy *Top Tunes for Violin*.
Further copies of this and the other books in the series
are available from your local music shop.

In case of difficulty, please contact the publisher direct:

The Sales Department
KEVIN MAYHEW LTD
Rattlesden
Bury St Edmunds
Suffolk IP30 0SZ

Phone 01449 737978
Fax 01449 737834

Please ask for our complete catalogue of outstanding Instrumental Music.

Acknowledgements

The publishers wish to express their gratitude to the copyright owners for
permission to use copyright material in this book. Details of these are given
underneath the individual tunes. All other tunes are copyright Kevin Mayhew Ltd.

Every effort has been made to trace the owners of copyright material, and we hope
that no copyright has been infringed. Pardon is sought and apology made if the
contrary be the case, and a correction will be made in any reprint of this book.

First published in Great Britain in 1996 by Kevin Mayhew Ltd.

© Copyright 1996 Kevin Mayhew Ltd.

ISBN 0 86209 817 3
Catalogue No: 3611200

Front cover illustration by Neil Pinchbeck
Cover design by Graham Johnstone and Veronica Ward

Music arrangements by Donald Thomson
Music Editor: Rosalind Dean
Music setting by Tracy Cracknell

Printed and bound in Great Britain by
Caligraving Limited Thetford Norfolk

Contents

THIS OLD MAN

Anon.

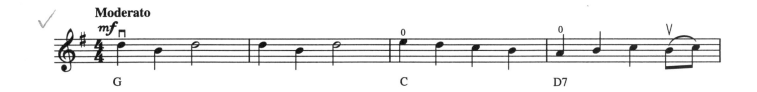

MICHAEL, ROW THE BOAT ASHORE

Traditional Melody

AU CLAIR DE LA LUNE

Traditional French Melody

ALL PEOPLE THAT ON EARTH DO DWELL

From the 'Genevan Psalter'

ODE TO JOY

Ludwig van Beethoven (1770-1827)

IL EST NÉ

Traditional French Melody

HERE WE GO ROUND THE MULBERRY BUSH

Traditional English Melody

THE VICAR OF BRAY

Traditional English Melody

MINUET IN G

Johann Sebastian Bach (1685-1750)

WHEN THE SAINTS GO MARCHING IN
Spiritual

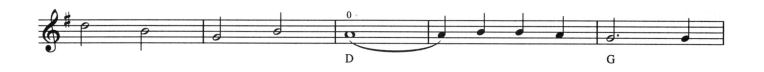

GOODNIGHT, LADIES
Traditional English Melody

THE CAN CAN

Jacques Offenbach (1819-1880)

SEE, THE CONQUERING HERO

George Frideric Handel (1685-1759)

SELLINGER'S ROUND

Anonymous 16th Century Melody

YE BANKS AND BRAES

Traditional Scottish Melody

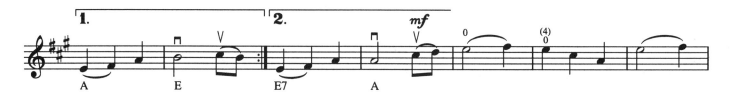

LILLIBURLERO

Traditional English Melody

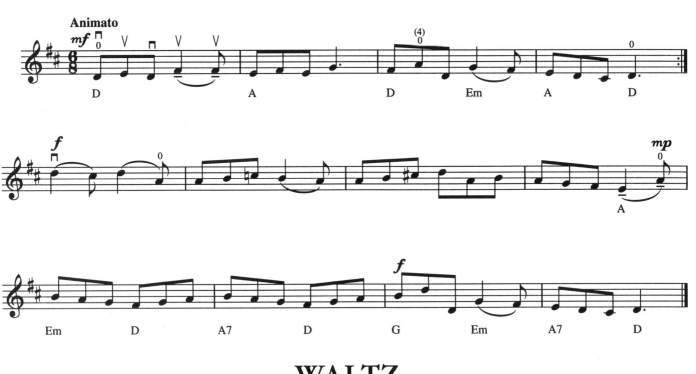

WALTZ

Johannes Brahms (1833-1897)

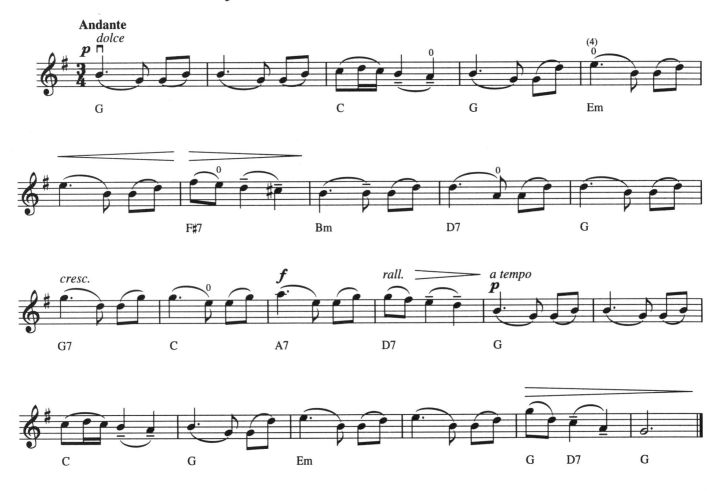

THE HARMONIOUS BLACKSMITH

George Frideric Handel (1685-1759)

FOR HE'S A JOLLY GOOD FELLOW

Traditional English Melody

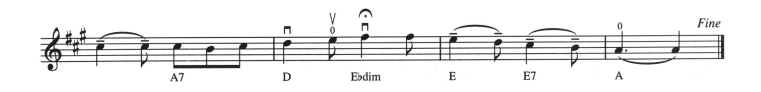

WALTZ from 'THE MERRY WIDOW'

Franz Lehar (1870-1948)

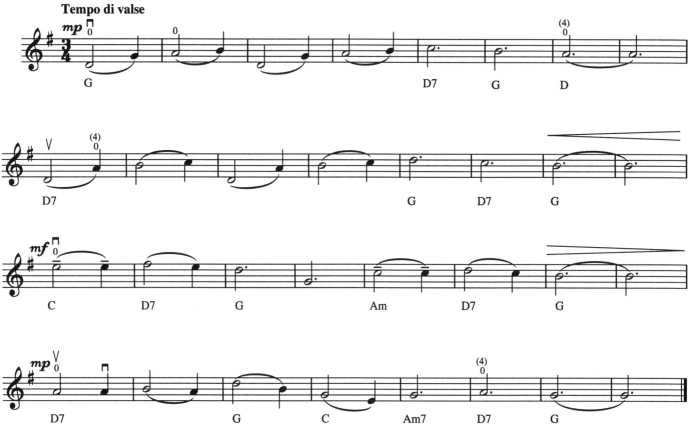

MEN OF HARLECH

Traditional Welsh Melody

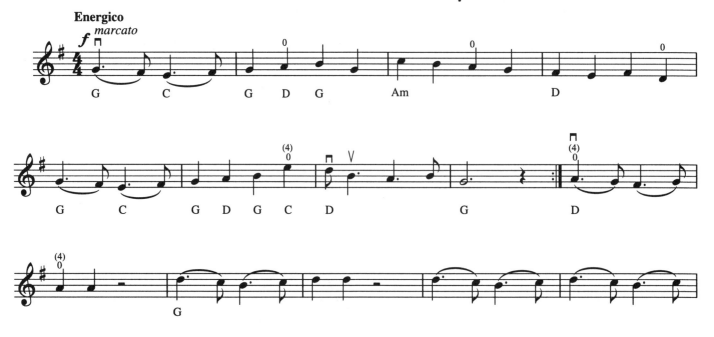

COCKLES AND MUSSELS

Traditional Irish Melody

15

SPRING from 'THE FOUR SEASONS'

Antonio Vivaldi (1678-1741)

LAND OF HOPE AND GLORY

Edward Elgar (1857-1934)

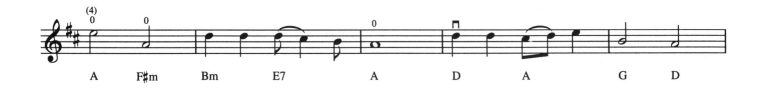

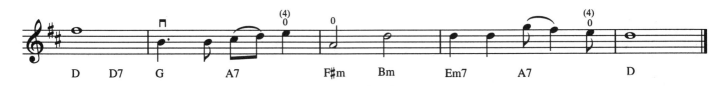

HOME ON THE RANGE

Daniel Kelly

HUMORESKE

Antonín Dvořák (1841-1904)

THE DRUNKEN SAILOR

Sea Shanty

ST ANTHONY CHORALE

Joseph Haydn (1732-1809)

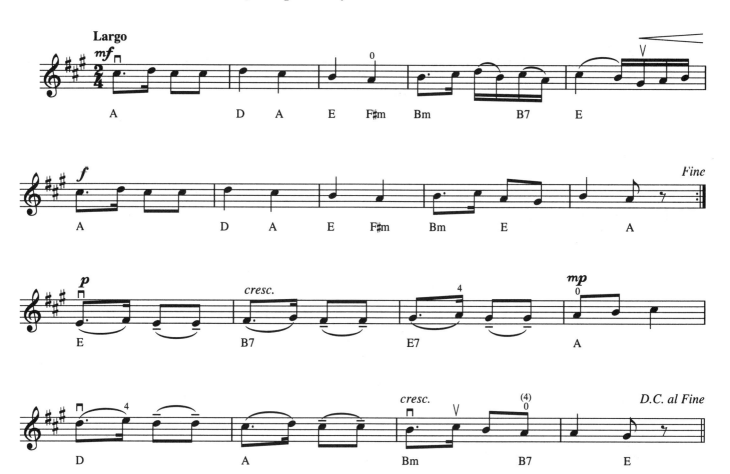

MINUET IN G

Ludwig van Beethoven (1770-1827)

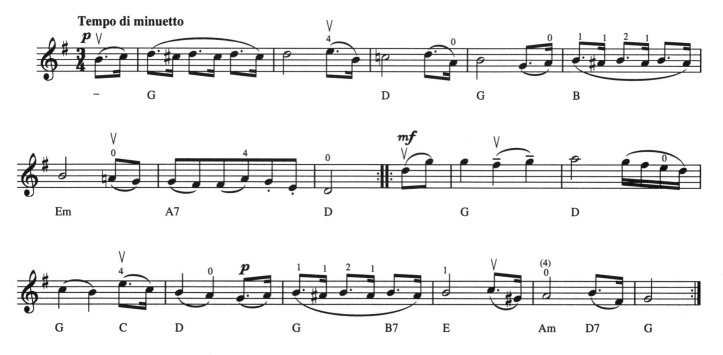

SWEET AND LOW

Joseph Barnby (1838-1896)

THEME from SYMPHONY NO 1

Johannes Brahms (1833-1897)

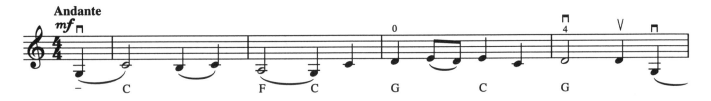

THE MAN WHO BROKE THE BANK
AT MONTE CARLO

Fred Gilbert

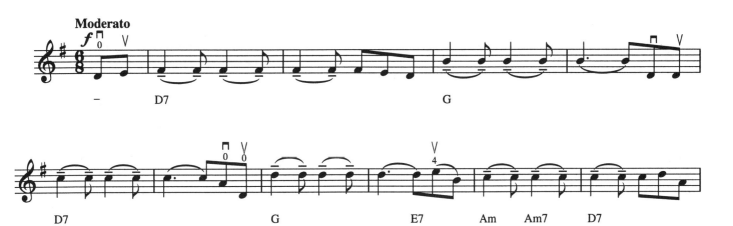

THE LASS OF RICHMOND HILL

James Hook (1746-1827)

CRADLE SONG

Franz Schubert (1797-1828)

SHEEP MAY SAFELY GRAZE

Johann Sebastian Bach (1685-1750)

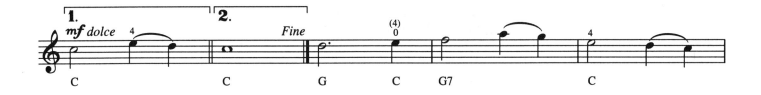

COMING THROUGH THE RYE
Traditional Scottish Melody

PIZZICATO POLKA

Johann Strauss II (1825-1899)

DANCE OF THE HOURS

Amilcare Ponchielli (1834-1886)

THE TROUT

Franz Schubert (1797-1828)

DANCE OF THE SUGAR-PLUM FAIRY

Peter Ilyich Tchaikovsky (1840-1893)

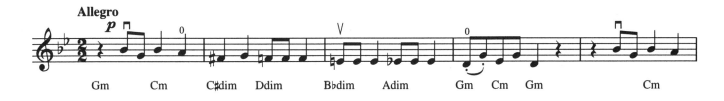

MY OLD MAN SAID FOLLOW THE VAN

Charles Collins and Fred Leigh

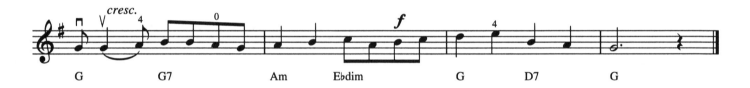

EINE KLEINE NACHTMUSIK

Wolfgang Amadeus Mozart (1756-1791)

RADETZKY MARCH

Johann Strauss (1804-1849)

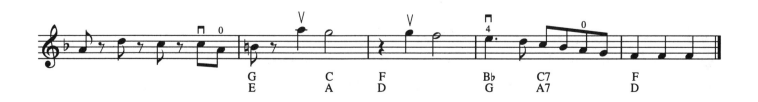

THE MARSEILLAISE

French National Anthem

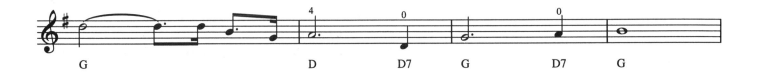

CAPRICE

Nicolo Paganini (1782-1840)

SAILORS' HORNPIPE

Sea Shanty

WILLIAM TELL OVERTURE

Gioachino Rossini (1792-1868)

MARCHE MILITAIRE

Franz Schubert (1797-1828)

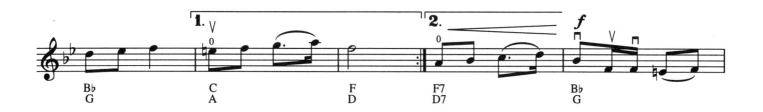

MARCH from 'THE NUTCRACKER'

Peter Ilyich Tchaikovsky (1840-1893)

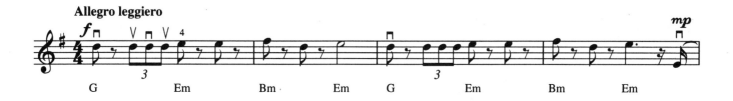

I DO LIKE TO BE BESIDE THE SEASIDE

John Glover-Kind